Scene In Harwich

A Scavenger Hunt of Sorts

Photography and Art by Marna Bate

Scene in Harwich, A Scavenger Hunt of Sorts

Thanks for support and help from Kimberly White, Cyndi Williams, my grandchildren, Waterlogue, Mary Moody, and Mark Carchidi.

To purchase a book email the author at SceneInHarwich@yahoo.com

ISBN-13: 978-0-578-78233-1

This book is a combination of beauty,
exploration and fun.

Your task is to fully and completely identify
each location in all of the images, for instance:
the old fire station on Bank Street,
or Brooks Free Library on Route 39,
or simply, a residence on Bank Street.

Try this by yourself or challenge friends and family to
see who can identify all locations first. When you have
traveled all the dirt roads, dead ends, and hidden
corners of Harwich, and answered
all that you can, turn to the last page for help.

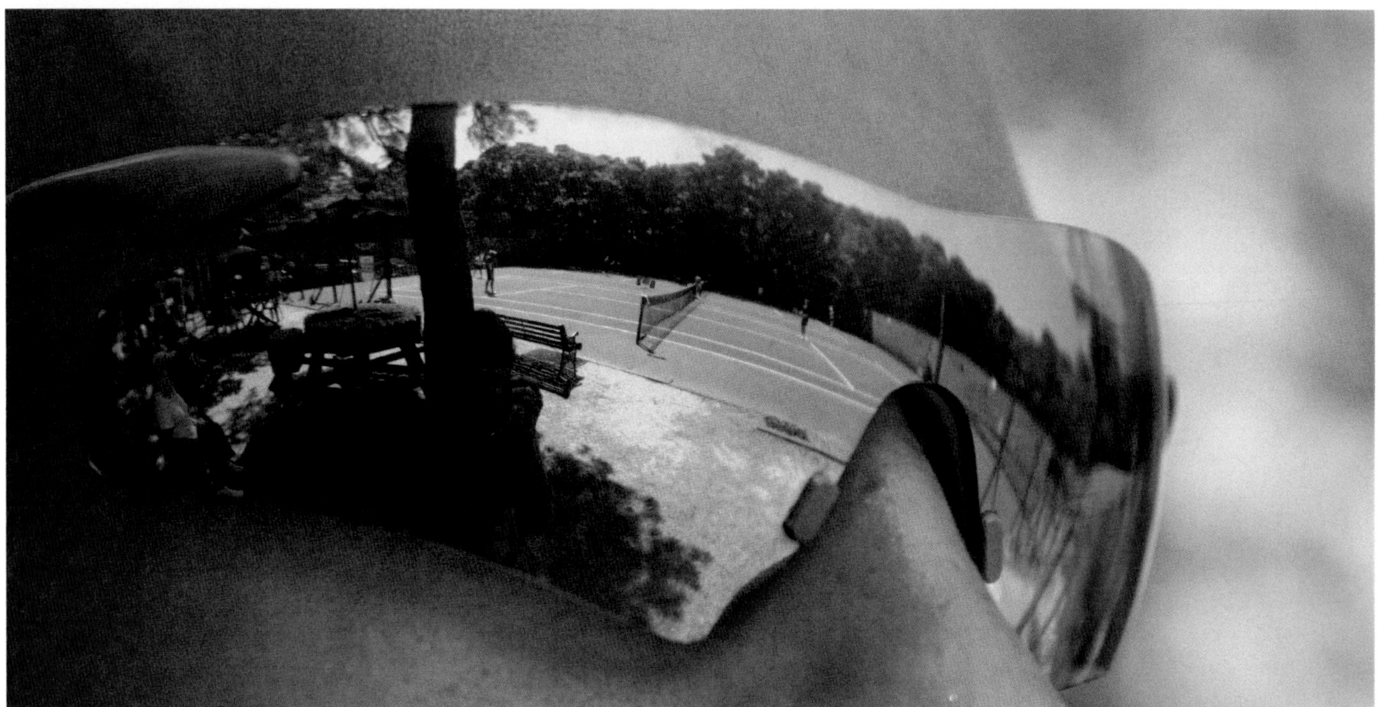

BROOKS
FREE
LIBRARY

Plywood
is for
Sissies!

Red River Beach kite surfers and one from the memory books.
Do you remember The Hollow?

PLUSH
GIRAFFE

THE PORT

SETUCKET
VILLAGE
580
WH LUTZ
ART
Studio Gallery
FOR SALE

74BANK
boutique
508.873.6886

NO
PARKING

Is this Red River Beach house gone?

BARBER SHOP

THE PORT

PLEASANT LAKE

10

The Nines
ART
GALLERY

CRUISE LINE
NANTUCKET FERRY
(508) 432-8999 • FREEDOMFERRY.COM
731

EZEKIEL 4:9
Superior
NUTRITION
TURBANA
PITAYA

THE
SANDY TURTLE

Monahan & Co

141
GINGERBREAD
HOUSE

10 YEN
MONKEYS

Near Bank Street Beach

The following is a list of locations in Harwich intended to help your search. Each location matches an image somewhere in this book. After you write your answers under the images, you may wish to write the page number next to the appropriate location on this list.

A residence on Bank Street
The Fire Bar at Ember, Route 28
Cape Cod Theater Company/ Harwich Junior Theater, Division Street
Brooks Park craft fair, Oak Street
Brooks Free Library, Route 39
The Port, Route 28 entrance to the Nautical Bar
Potters Field off Oak Street
Residence on Smith Street
First Congregational Church, Route 124 and Route 39
Ace Hardware, Route 28
The old fire station, Bank Street
Red River Beach
The Hollow, Cranberry Harvest Festival, Oak Street and Route 39
Pleasant Bay, Route 28
Thatchers Cranberries, Great Western Road
Dr. Gravity's Kite Shop, Route 28
Harwich Cultural Center, Sisson Road
First Congregational Church, Route 124 and Route 39
The Traditional Barber Shop, Route 28
Hinckleys Pond, Route 124
The Augustus Snow House, Route28
Wyndemere Bluffs Beach
Deep Hole Road toward Red River Beach
Bell's Neck Bridge and the Herring River
The Port, Sea Street entrance
Atlantic Avenue Beach, Snow Inn condominiums in the distance
Hinckleys Pond off Route 124
Monahan's now Murphy's General Store, Route 28
Gingerbread House on Division Street

A Residence, Gorham Road
Art in the Park with The Guild of Harwich Artists at Doane Park, Route 28
Herring River Bridge and town landing, Route 28
Sand Pond, Great Western Road
Any street with a bench by the sea in Harwichport
W H Lutz Art Studio and Gallery, Route 28
Brooks Park pickleball, Oak Street
Stop and Shop at Routes 137 and Route 39
Sea Style Living Shop, 74 Bank Street
Cranberry Golf Course, Oak Street
Harwich Community Center, Oak Street
A residence, Queen Anne Road and Samoset Road
Cape Cod's Irish Pub, Route 28, West Harwich
A residence, Freeman Street
Sativa, Route 28
North Road Bridge crabbers
Red River Beach
The Treasure Chest, Queen Anne Road
Hawksnest Pond
Ocean Cove Condominiums, Route 28, West Harwich
Herring River off North Road
Bud's Go Karts, Sisson Road
A waterway off Hoyt Road
Cape Roots Market and Cafe and Cranberry Liquors on Route 28
A residence on Bay View Road
Locarios Tennis Center off Route 28
Saquatucket Harbor, Route 28
Brax Landing, Saquatucket Harbor, Route 28
Hunter's Golf & Tennis Shop, Route 28

Pilgrim Congregational Church, Route 28
Whitehouse Field off Oak Street
Lexaco, Route 28
Pleasant Lake General Store, Route 124
Nathan Walker Road off Spruce Road
Grand Slam Entertainment, Bumper Boats, Route 28
The Nines Art Gallery, Route 28
Winstead Inn and Beach Resort, Braddock Street
Bell's Neck Bridge, West Harwich
The Freedom Cruise Line at Saquatucket Harbor, Route 28
J.Bar, Sea Street
A section of the bike path off Bell's Neck Road
Windsong Antiques, Sisson Road and Route 28
Oak Street on July 23, 2019
White Flowers, Bank Street
The Sandy Turtle, Sea Street
Cape Sea Grill, Sea Street
Bank Street Bogs
The Mason Jar, Route 28
Red River Beach
Residences on Ocean Avenue
Albro House, Route 39
A residence, Joe Anne Way
North Road, West Harwich
Harwich Town Hall, Route 39
Wychmere Harbor, Snow Inn Road
Wequassett Resort, Route 28
The Three Monkeys, Route 28
The Melrose, Route 28, Harwichport
A short walk from Bank Street Beach

'Bird's Eye View' photograph by J. G. Brackett

Made in the USA
Middletown, DE
29 November 2020